Beyo
Park Gates

C000202808

Beyond the Park Gates

Eleven steps to financial freedom and personal happiness

Julie Wilson and Sarah Smelik

COPPICE
PUBLISHING

Published by Coppice Publishing 2015
Copyright © Julie Wilson & Sarah Smelik 2015
Julie Wilson and Sarah Smelik have asserted their right to be identified as the authors of this work.

www.beyondtheparkgates.com

All rights reserved.
This book is sold or supplied subject to the condition that it shall not, by way of trade or otherwise:

a) be reproduced or copied in whole or in part and in any form or by any means without the publisher's consent; or

b) be lent, resold, hired out, or otherwise circulated without the publisher's prior consent in any form of binding or cover other than that in which it is published and without a similar condition including this condition being imposed on the subsequent acquirer.

The moral rights of the author have been asserted.

First published in the United Kingdom in 2015
by Coppice Publishing
Electronic edition published in 2015 by Coppice Publishing
Coppice Publishing
17 Hunters Way, York YO24 1JL

A CIP catalogue record for this book is available from the British Library.

ISBN 978-0-9555-199-1-8

Edited by Sarah Smelik
Design and Typesetting by Ned Hoste
Printed by CPI Group (UK)

What people are saying about
Beyond the Park Gates

"It's a lovely story with many useful tactics and ideas.
It tells you exactly what you should do and that it is
different for everybody."

"What I really like about the book is that it talks about
enjoying the journey and actively participating rather
than just thinking about the destination."

"It is well written and easy to read with nice small chunks
to digest."

Stefan Haase, Director, Strategy 4 Growth

"I love the story and it certainly made me think."
"I cannot emphasise how wonderful it is. Absolutely amazing."

Andrew Wilkinson, Director, Britcab Ltd

"Very useful suggestions and steps, wrapped up in an engaging story, and I will apply them to my own working life."

"It really makes you think how small manageable changes can make a very big difference."

Jill Andrews, Director, Andrews Signs and Engravers Ltd

Contents

Forewords

If you've come across me before you know that I am a straight-talking Yorkshire woman who likes to call a spade a spade. I sometimes get into trouble and upset people, and that's too bad, but at least it means they listen! I would rather speak the blunt truth than spout softly softly sugar-coated nonsense. And I hope you would too.

So, here's what I think: If you are not living the life you want to live, then it's your fault. Yes, I mean you! No-one else. You can blame Fate, you can blame your parents, your boss, your kids, the postman, the past, the pothole in the road, whoever or whatever you want to. And if you do that, then good luck to you. But the longer you deny taking responsibility for what is happening in your life right now, then the longer you will put off living the life you want.

Got it? If you have, then read on. If not, then put this book in the WC and use it instead of Andrex. Or better still, pass it on to someone who might actually get some use out of it. You see, it's pointless having this book if you do not actually do what it tells you to. So many people talk about wanting to change their lives, but only the very few are bothered to get up off their backsides to do something about it.

It's not luck that I am where I am today, that I have left behind the council estate where I grew up and ended up co-owning a multi-million pound financial planning company. It has involved lots of hard work, persistence and constant self-education. On the way, I've learned that there are a number of fundamental, timeless principles that myself and other successful people implement in our daily lives. It's not rocket science, or some mysterious secret skill exclusive to wealthy entrepreneurs. It is a list of simple things that you can all do, everyday, which can change your life for the better.

I have to mention my two favourite books, which inspired me to co-write this with Sarah Smelik - 'The Richest Man in Babylon' by Charles Conrad, and 'Who Moved My Cheese' by Dr Spencer Johnson, both of which take less than an hour to read. If you haven't come across them I suggest you get them immediately! There are loads more that champion the principles of success, but not many do it as succinctly as those two.

I wanted to pass on my own interpretation of these principles, which have been so instrumental in my own success, to as many people as possible, and decided a fictional book like those that inspired me, would be the best way to go about it. But I am a bit 'left-brained' – I love facts, statistics and numbers which would bore the pants off most people. I needed to 'borrow' the creative right side of someone else's brain, which is why I turned to Sarah.

Sarah has the knack of turning my left-brained stuff into engaging and readable copy. So we worked together on 'Beyond the Park Gates' – I came up with the principles, and she turned them into what I think is a fantastic and simple story about one woman's journey from a life of apathetic acceptance to one of financial freedom and happiness.

I hope you enjoy it. Please share it with those you know, and those you think might benefit from these principles. And last of all, be the one who gets off your backside and does what it says!

Julie Wilson

When Julie asked me to write a story based upon a number of principles that had helped her become successful, I was, at first, delighted, and then, stumped. What to write? A blank page stared intimidatingly back at me, daring me to come up with a half-decent plot.

But writing a book is just like one of the principles that Julie had talked about – it's not so much about how quick or how long a journey is, it's about taking that first step. And that first step is often the hardest. Like Katie in the book, I took the first step by writing one paragraph, followed by another, and another, and suddenly, I had a chapter. And then I just kept going, paragraph by paragraph. That's not to say that it didn't undergo many edits and changes along the way, of course it did, but once I had taken that first step, written that first paragraph, I knew I would ultimately get to those two most important words – 'The End'.

Like I hope Katie's story will be to those who read this book, Julie's own story is inspirational to me. From where she came to where she is now, is a remarkable achievement. But one of the lessons I have learned from her is that you can read and learn all you like, but unless you take action and do the things the experts tell you to do, your life will not change. It's like that old adage 'If you keep doing the same thing, you can expect the same result'. So if you want your life to change, then you have to do something to make it change.

So perhaps reading this book is your first step – I hope it is, because not only is it an easy and, I hope, entertaining read, it also contains the fundamental principles of success that every single one of us can implement to achieve the life we want.

So come on, step in, and see what lies beyond the park gates.

Sarah Smelik

About the authors

Julie Wilson grew up on a council estate and left school at 16 to work as an office junior in a local accountancy firm. She now co-owns a multi-million-pound independent financial advice company in York, and has spent her whole working life in the finance industry. Over the years, she became an avid student of tax planning and is now a Chartered Financial Planner and Fellow of the Personal Finance Society, one of the highest qualifications in the business. Julie has made it her life's work to help as many people as possible become financial secure.

Sarah Smelik grew up in North Yorkshire and hails from a writing family, with her father being author Nicholas Rhea, a prolific writer most well known for the Constable series which inspired TV hit Heartbeat. Sarah trained as a journalist, and then went into freelance writing and editing in 1994. She now specialises in business development projects and project-managing books into print, although she continues to write, edit and publish books in the creative, business and marketing fields.

Bench One

A perfect day for sitting on a bench

Katie Connor slumped onto the park bench and stared at the bag containing the sandwich she'd just bought from the deli on the high street. She wasn't particularly hungry, but the office rules were that you couldn't eat at your desk, and that you had to take your lunch break when you were told to.

She didn't normally come out of the office during lunch, she always had so much work to do that it was easier just to head to the staff canteen for a quick bite to eat. In fact, she couldn't remember the last time she had actually felt fresh air on her face during her lunch break. She leant back and looked out towards the busy street that ran alongside the park, at all the people going about their lives. She wished she could be one of those, not having to go back into the stuffy office where everyone around her seemed as unhappy as she was to be there.

But she had bills to pay, kids to feed and a house to run so she didn't have a choice but to go back to work. Her mind wandered to her kids. They would come home from school ravenous, like they did every day, and what did she have in for tea? Not a lot, so it might well have to be something from the freezer again. She cursed under her breath as she remembered that she had forgotten to put the washing in this morning - Abi would need her PE kit clean for tomorrow. She sighed heavily, and stared down at her sandwich again.

"Beautiful day, isn't it?"

Katie jumped as the loud voice interrupted her thoughts. She turned and realized there was an elderly man sitting at the other end of the bench who was looking straight at her. She hadn't noticed him.

"A perfect day for sitting on a park bench," he smiled.

"Erm…" Katie looked up to the sky. It was crystal clear blue, and the sun felt warm on her face. She hadn't even registered that it was sunny until now.

"And look, the blossom is beginning to peep out. It won't be long before those trees will be in full bloom," he said.

"Oh, yes," replied Katie. She felt a bit uncomfortable. Strangers didn't talk to each other on park benches. It was odd – what if he was some kind of weirdo?

"Do you come to this park a lot?"

Ok, he was definitely some kind of weirdo who wanted to find out her movements so that he could kidnap her or flash at her or something next time he saw her.

"I really must get back to work," she said quickly and stood up.

"That's a shame," he said, "to have to go back inside on such a lovely day. That's why I always make the effort to come out on days like this. It really lifts the spirits."

Katie fidgeted with her sandwich bag. She felt awkward, standing there, resisting the temptation to run away while trying to appear as if she wasn't remotely concerned that he might be some kind of pervert. She glanced at him, and he was still smiling directly at her. He didn't look like she imagined a pervert to look, but instead had a kindly face with eyes that twinkled as he smiled. He was dressed in a rather old-fashioned woollen three-piece suit, with a gold watch-chain visible from one of the pockets of the waistcoat. He wore a matching trilby hat and his shoes were highly polished brown leather brogues. If he was a pervert, he was a very well-dressed one. She guessed his age must be somewhere in the early seventies.

"Oh, there's Joe! Now then Joe, how are you? Beautiful day! How is the flower garden?"

"Mr Smith, I'm not surprised to see you here on a day like this!" Another man, who looked like a well-worn gardener, appeared from behind Katie and went to sit on the bench next to Mr Smith. Side by side, they looked like a very odd couple. While Mr Smith was immaculately turned out, Joe was scruffy, unkempt and filthy, which Katie supposed you might expect of a gardener. He was a similar age to Mr Smith though, and Katie thought it unusual that he'd still be working rather than taking it easy in retirement. She couldn't wait for the day when she could retire and put her feet up! But then she remembered, how would she ever be able to put her feet up when she had no money saved for retirement and the state pension was a laughable amount? It might not even exist by the time she retired the way things were going! She sighed again, knowing it was just one more of life's countless worries that she just had to put up with.

"I have some glorious blooms, Mr Smith! You must come and see them. Mrs Smith would have loved what I've got now."

"I certainly will. Let me introduce you to...I'm sorry I didn't catch your name?"

"Katie," said Katie before she could stop herself. Oh no! Now two strange old men in the park knew her name. Maybe they were the masterminds behind some kind of human trafficking ring...She should have just stayed in the office. Serves her right for doing something different. That'll teach her.

"Pleased to meet you Katie! You've chosen the perfect day to come down to the park. Sorry, have I stolen your place?"

"Er...no, I was just about to go back to work."

"Oh, poor you having to go back inside."

Mr. Smith nodded in agreement. "And she's only just got here. Such a shame you have to rush off, Katie, when there's so much beauty to find in the park today."

"There certainly is, Mr Smith," said Joe. "And those roses Mrs Smith used to love, we have even more now and they're doing brilliantly. In six or eight weeks they'll knock your socks off!"

"Will they? They are beautiful, and so fragrant. Do you think I could take a few stems from those flowering now? They'll fill the house with their scent and remind me of her!"

"Of course Mr Smith! Let's go and get you some."

The two men stood up. "Would you like to come, Katie? It really is worth a look," said Mr Smith.

Katie shook her head, "Thank you, no, I must get back."

"What a shame. Very well then, enjoy the rest of your day Katie. Lovely to meet you, bye."

Katie watched as the two men pottered off, chattering happily, and obviously savouring the sights around them as they walked. She suddenly felt very silly. It was clear they were just two friendly old men enjoying the weather and the park. And poor Mr Smith, to have lost the wife he obviously loved dearly. How could she have misjudged him? "I am so bloody stupid," she muttered.

Katie still had a good forty minutes of her lunch break left, but daren't sit back down and eat her sandwich now. What if they came back and saw her? They'd know she had lied to them and she would look a real fool.

Instead, she ate her sandwich as she usually did, by herself, in the staff canteen and looked around her as she did so. She was struck by how much the expressions on people's faces contrasted with Mr Smith's. Everyone here looked downtrodden with the woes of life, whereas Mr Smith looked - well - happy! She stared wistfully out of the window, towards the sun, which she now realised she missed an awful lot.

Katie wished she could be happy and positive like Mr. Smith, but she knew she couldn't, not with everything she had to contend with. Life just seemed to get harder, and more expensive too. How she was going to pay off that credit card, she had no idea. She was still paying off last year's holiday, and the kids were already talking about their next one. She was hoping life would get better one day, and was sure that if she worked hard enough and kept her head down, it surely would. One day.

Bench Two

Never listen to Negative's elf talk

The next day, the weather was just as glorious, and Katie found herself looking forward to having lunch in the park again. If she happened upon Mr. Smith, this time, she would stay and chat to him and would apologise for being rude and rushing off.

She bought a sandwich and a coffee from the deli again, then went back to the same park bench and found herself surprisingly disappointed when Mr. Smith wasn't there. She could see Joe, though, some way away, working on one of the park flower beds. He paused for a moment, and rested his arm on his garden fork, then waved when he caught sight of her. She waved back, and felt a smile automatically creep onto her lips. How kind, she thought, for him to acknowledge her, even though he'd only seen her for a few minutes yesterday. It was a welcome change from feeling invisible.

As Katie ate her sandwich, she looked around at the park. Really looked. She had walked past it hundreds of times, and even sat on this same bench a few times, but was usually so wrapped up in her own thoughts that she had never taken time to look around and absorb it.

It was a gorgeous park – in fact, more like a huge garden than a park. It had lots of winding paths, flowerbeds, shrubs and trees. She had never gone further than where she was now, never had a reason to before, so she couldn't say what or where the paths led to. And something struck her now that she had not really noticed before – the sounds. She could hear the joyous cries of small children laughing and playing, a dog barking while it waited for its owner to throw a ball, birds twittering and singing backwards and forwards to one another, the animated conversation of two mothers pushing babies in prams in front of her. It was as if she had suddenly woken up to a new world, like she had opened her eyes and ears to it for the very first time. And yet she walked past it every single working day. How had she missed all this? She should bring the kids down here at the weekend, she decided. They could have ice cream! They'd love that.

"Katie! How lovely to see you again!"

"Mr Smith!"

"I must say Katie, you look rather cheerful today."

"I was just thinking how beautiful this place is. I've never appreciated it before."

"Isn't it? It's funny how we don't always appreciate what is right on our doorstep until we actually take time to look properly."

Katie nodded. "Would you...would you like to join me?"

"Well that would be delightful, thank you Katie, but might I be so bold as to suggest we walk down to the next bench? It has a view I'd love you to see, and it's not so much further. I always think that it does one good to change one's view regularly!"

"Of course."

As they walked, Katie's mind was full of guilt at what she had thought when she had first met Mr. Smith. They strolled further into the park, all the while Mr. Smith pointing out plants, trees, shrubs and wildlife.

"This is such an amazing place. I had no idea," she said.

They reached the bench, and Mr. Smith motioned for her to sit down. Before her stretched out a gently shimmering pond, with water lilies and irises just coming into bloom. Groups of ducks fussed around their little posses of offspring, while geese gossiped in groups near the water's edge.

"I can't believe I never even knew this was here."

"It's amazing what you find when you take a few extra steps," said Mr. Smith, "And amazing what you miss if you don't look properly, like what's written on this bench."

Katie turned, and there was an inscription stretching across the top of the wooden seat which she hadn't taken any notice of when she sat down.

She laughed.

"What's so funny?" asked Mr. Smith.

"The inscription. There's a spelling mistake. It says 'Never listen to Negative's elf talk.'" Katie laughed again, "Of course, it should say 'negative self talk.'"

"Should it?" Mr Smith raised an eyebrow, before continuing, "Let me tell you a story. There was a man called Fred, and he was very sad, downtrodden and lonely. Life had given him a rotten deal, and nothing ever seemed to go right for him. He hated his job, had debt up to his eyeballs, and his wife had left him for another man. On each of his shoulders sat an elf. The elves stayed there all the time, every day, all day and all night. One elf was named Positive, the other was named Negative. Both elves were identical, and very vociferous.

"Negative said things like 'You hate your job, but what else can you do? You're not good enough to do anything else. No wonder your wife left you, you're boring and will never amount to anything. Who's going to love someone like you? Don't even think about getting rich either. People like you never get rich because the rich look down on you, and they don't care about anyone but themselves. You don't want to be like that, do you Fred?'

"All the while, Positive was also trying to make himself heard: 'You are good enough Fred, you can change your life. You just have to believe in yourself and listen to me! You have so much potential in you Fred, you just have to realize it. You can be rich if you want to, and imagine all the good you could do when you have money? Think of the life you could lead? Of course you will be loved, you are a good person, Fred.'

"But for some reason, Fred gave all his attention to Negative's elf talk, and so Negative's voice grew louder and louder, and Positive's grew feinter and feinter until he couldn't be heard at all. Fred ended his days a broke, lonely and bitter man. But it could all have been so different if only he had taken notice of Positive's elf talk.

"You see, we all have our elves, Katie, we just can't see them. But boy, we can hear them! The thing which most people don't understand is that we CHOOSE which one we listen to. Sadly, many people choose to listen to – and more importantly, believe - Negative's elf talk without understanding that only they have the power to shut him up."

Katie smiled as she imagined two little elves sitting on her shoulders vying for her attention. "Mr. Smith, can I apologise for yesterday?"

"Apologise? Whatever for?"

"Well, for not being friendly."

"But you were friendly."

"I wasn't very. You see, I didn't know you, so I just assumed…"

"…you assumed I was not to be trusted because I was a total stranger. And my dear, that is an absolutely understandable judgment to make. Why should you trust someone you have just met?"

"I realised afterwards that you were just being kind. It was so stupid of me."

"Who's that talking?"

Katie frowned, then understood what he was getting at. "That'll be Negative's elf talk."

"You were anything but stupid – you were sensible enough to come to the conclusion to give me another chance once you had digested the information you were faced with. Very clever of you. You'll be amazed how many people I manage to scare off! And I am delighted you are back because one of the things I like most in the world is to show people what is in this park that they are usually just too busy to appreciate."

"Well I'm sorry if I appeared unfriendly."

"To be honest, I never even gave it a second thought. Have you heard the phrase 'Whatever you think of me is none of my business'? No? Well, it is something I learned to live by, and once you truly understand that phrase, life becomes a whole lot easier. Whatever you thought of me yesterday was truly none of my business, so it didn't bother me at all."

Katie laughed, "That's a good phrase. I might use it."

"Use it, and more importantly, believe it! I must say, seeing you today, I would think I was looking at a different person than the one I saw yesterday. You seemed very down, if I may be so bold."

Katie nodded. "Was it that obvious?"

"It was. But you know what, I bet you have spent too much time in your past listening..."

"...to Negative's elf talk!" laughed Katie.

"Exactly! So the trick is to recognise when that mischievous little elf is talking to you, and ask him to politely shush, because you want to hear what Positive has to say."

"What if Positive has nothing to say?"

"Positive ALWAYS has something to say! Remember, he's just as vociferous as Negative. It's just that he might not be loud enough for you to hear him. But if you pay him enough attention, and ignore Negative, he'll soon find his voice! In fact, I wouldn't be surprised if he's saying right now, 'Katie, I'm so proud of you for coming back to the park and keeping Mr. Smith company. And well done for apologising - that takes real courage, even if Mr Smith didn't think you needed to! Three cheers for Katie!'"

Katie laughed again, "You are funny, Mr. Smith. I wish I could stay here all afternoon, but sadly, I need to go back to work now, but I will listen out for my Positive elf! "

"Don't forget it's just as important to be aware when Negative elf is talking to you too because we can be so used to hearing him that we forget to silence him."

"I will..."

"And what people think of you...?"

"...is none of my business. Got it! Thank you Mr. Smith. To next time."

Bench Three

Always pay yourself first

The next time Katie saw Mr. Smith was a few days later. He wasn't on either of the first two benches, so she decided to walk on further into the park, taking a path she had never walked before. She found him sitting on another bench apparently watching the world go by.

"Ah, Katie, you found me! Have a seat. Not so many in the park today. The weather is not as nice, so they've stayed away. I do feel they miss out though, because there is still plenty to see, like that grey squirrel over there. Look at him scurrying around at the bottom of that tree."

"He's very busy, isn't he? He looks like he's lost something."

"He's looking for acorns. He will have buried some when they fell in the autumn so that he has a store of food available for when it is scarce, and he is trying to find them again."

"You would think he'd remember where he'd left them."

"They often don't."

"What a waste of effort burying them in the first place then!" said Katie.

"Not really, when you think that wild animals like squirrels are responsible for keeping our population of splendid oak trees going. They scatter their acorns over a wide area, and those they can't find will potentially germinate and become a new oak tree. It's the only way the oak can reproduce, as its seeds are too heavy to be dispersed on the wind."

"I never knew that! Clever little squirrel!"

"Isn't he? Look, he's scampering over to the wild meadow just over there."

"Oh, he's disappeared now," said Katie, looking towards to the meadow. "It's an unusual part of the park, that bit, not like the rest at all."

"It is, they keep it like that deliberately to encourage and preserve our native wildlife. It is so different to the rest of the park and yet just as impressive with its long grasses and wildflowers that attract so many insects. It really is lovely, even on a day like today. You just have to come prepared for the weather, don't you think?" Mr Smith had a woollen overcoat on over his suit.

"Well, now that I've started coming out more, I find I miss it if I don't," said Katie, nodding. "I can't wait for lunch time now! I even asked my colleagues if they wanted to come with me, but they said it wasn't a nice enough day."

"It is often the way, my dear, when the weather turns a bit inclement, most people tend to retreat!"

"I think I was like that, until I realized it was so much nicer being out here even when it isn't the most beautiful day in the world."

"Exactly. Anyway, my dear, how are your elves?"

Katie laughed. "Well, now I have learned to listen properly, I realise just how noisy Negative is! He seems to talk ALL the time. But now I know, I can hear him much more clearly, and can choose not to listen any more. I found the more I listen to Positive, the more Positive I become. Life seems, well, less miserable!"

"It does, doesn't it? And does that make you enjoy work more?"

Katie sighed. "Not really. But it makes it more bearable, I suppose."

"Why are you doing that job if you don't enjoy it?"

"Because I get paid, and I can't afford not to."

Mr. Smith paused for a moment, looking thoughtfully into the distance. "If money was no object, and you could do whatever you wanted in the world, what would it be?"

"Apart from lounge by the pool somewhere hot and drink champagne all day? I have no idea. I just can't imagine a life where I can do what I like when I like. People who can do that are very lucky."

"Do you think so? That it's down to luck?"

"Well it must play a part. I'm not a lucky person, good things just never seem to happen to me."

"Well, I'm sorry to hear that. But there is something you can do, right now, to start turning your life around."

"Really? What?"

Mr Smith pointed to the inscription on the bench.

"Another inscription?," said Katie, before reading, " 'Always pay yourself first.' Pay myself? With what? What does it mean?"

"It means that with any money you ever get in, you need to make sure you pay yourself some of that money, at least ten percent. Put it away, and keep it."

"But I have no money left over at the end of the month. I can't afford to put any away."

"First of all, you do it as soon as you get paid. Secondly, you must afford it. How's your coffee, by the way?"

"It's nice, from the deli on the high street. They do really good coffee."

"And good sandwiches....? Let me guess, about £5 in total?"

"Oh, I see what you're getting at! But it's just a little treat that makes me feel good. I don't get it every day, only a couple of times a week."

"So, that's £10 a week, for 48 weeks a year, if you factor in holidays. £480 for 240 coffees and sandwiches."

Katie was impressed at his ability to calculate so quickly. "Oooo - that's quite a lot, isn't it? And I have to admit that I often go three times a week. It doesn't occur to me how much it all adds up because it doesn't seem very much at the time. And because I'm not especially happy at work, it's my little pick-me-up."

"And we all need those from time to time. But problems arise when its cumulative effect becomes detrimental to your future financial security. It's known as the latte effect – the long-term cost of all the little fripperies that we spend our loose change on on a daily basis. I'm sure you can think of a few other things you spend money on during the week that if you are honest with yourself, you don't really need to do."

Katie nodded, "I can. The children buy sandwiches and drinks from the school canteen. I could make their sandwiches and they could take drinks with them. It would actually save quite a lot of money."

"So you see, if you really, and I mean really want to start turning your life around, you will find a way to do it. And do you have any direct debits coming out of your account?"

"Well, yes, quite a few. I'm not sure how many exactly."

A knowing look had entered Mr Smith's eyes. "When was the last time you did a proper overhaul of your accounts, just to make sure you really are only paying for the things you need to?"

"I don't think I ever have. I left all that to my husband, but since he left, I've not really checked...I've been a bit neglectful, haven't I?"

"You are not unlike many other people in your position. It's just that if you do have a look, you'll be surprised at what might be going out of your bank account that needn't. And that money would be put to far better use if it was going towards your future."

"I've never really been interested in money..."

"Many people aren't until it's too late! And they lose so much along the way. If only they had paid attention, and done something with that that money, they would be far better off today. If I may be so bold, Katie, how old are you? You look young enough to be my granddaughter."

"And you are a charmer! I'm 35."

Mr. Smith smiled, "So, you started working when you were still a teenager?"

Katie nodded. "I had part-time jobs from the age of 15, so I've been working for twenty years. Good grief. That sounds like a long time. Time flies..."

"It does...as does money, out of your pocket, if you are not careful."

"Imagine if I had started putting money away then...I earned about £30 a week waitressing and I did that for five years before I got a job with the council in the admin department when I was 20."

"So, say you worked 48 weeks a year, and saved three pounds a week for five years." Mr. Smith totted the amounts up in his head, "£720."

"And then I was paid better at the council. It was a proper full-time job and I took home £600 a month after tax. I remember getting my first proper pay cheque - I thought I'd won the lottery!"

"And did you start putting any money away then?"

Katie laughed as if the suggestion was ridiculous. "No. It all went on clothes, nights out and partying! A lot of partying!" She smiled at the memories.

"I can imagine it was a lot of fun, and you did absolutely right to enjoy yourself. How long were you with the council?"

"Eight years."

"So if you'd started putting ten per cent aside then..."

"Oh, don't go there, it's too painful..."

"£5,760. And if that money had been invested wisely at the time..."

"It would be worth a lot more now. It seems so simple - all for one less night out or pair of shoes a month all those years ago. Now, I usually have to choose between getting myself something new, or something for the children. If only..."

"Now those are two words I don't like to hear. 'If only' means regret. Regret nothing. Just learn. You had no idea what to do with your money then, no one had told you how to manage it, so you must not blame yourself. This country is very bad at teaching our young ones how to make themselves financially free, when really, the whole place would be in a much better state if we taught a few simple techniques to them in the classroom. But now, you can pass what you learn on to your children. And it's not too late for you to start now, of course."

"Isn't it? You really think I can sort myself out?"

"I know you can, if you truly want to. You just have to believe it yourself. And keep listening to Positive."

Just then, a little dog trotted along the path in front of them, with a loose lead flapping about its collar. Katie leapt up and caught hold of it before it ran off.

"What a sweet little boy you are! Who do you belong to?" she said, allowing it to sniff her hand before stroking it's head. The dog started to wag its tail and tried to jump up and lick Katie's face as she crouched down. "No, down boy. Sit," she said firmly, and held the palm of her hand out flat. The dog did what he was told. "Isn't he a gorgeous springer spaniel, Mr. Smith? He's got a lovely, glossy coat. Someone looks after him well." She looked up to see if she could spot the owner.

"He sure is, and he obviously likes you. He certainly listens to you too!"

"Oh, I love dogs. I grew up with them and my dad taught me how to train them, so I do know a thing or two. I'd love to have one, but it's not really practical with me working so much. And our house is very small."

Sure enough, a few moments later, a middle-aged lady came running along the path panting and shouting, "Hamish! Hamish! Oh, there you are, you naughty boy! Running away like that! Thank you so much. He's is very naughty, he keeps escaping. I don't know what to do with him."

"He's a lovely dog and he's got such a shiny coat," said Katie.

"Oh, he's adorable to look at. But my goodness, he's a challenge to look after. I really don't know what to do."

"Have you tried dog training classes?"

"Can you believe that no-one does it around here? I've looked. The nearest person is across the other side of town and I simply don't have the time to go traipsing all the way over there. You seem very good with dogs,"

"Well, I grew up with them...

"Look how well he's behaving for you! I wish he was like that for me. I don't suppose you could help me, could you? I at my wits' end! I'd be happy to pay you. Please?"

For a few moments, Katie heard Negative's elf talk loud and clear: "Don't even think about it Katie. You have a job. It'll be too much to take on. What if you're no good at it? What if it goes wrong? What if...."

But one glance at Mr Smith's beaming expression soon silenced him, and allowed her to hear Positive say: "Go on, Katie, go for it!"

"I'd love to help you," she said.

Bench Four

Take responsibility for you

The following week, Katie was eager to meet up with Mr Smith again. How much had happened in seven days! She couldn't wait to tell him, he'd be so pleased with her!

As she had come to expect, he wasn't on any of the benches she had visited before, and she had to walk even further into the park to find him, which she did, sitting on a new bench overlooking a stunning flower garden.

Before she could speak, he said: "Ah, there you are Katie! Would you look at those spectacular flowers, they've been so well tended by Joe! He spent so much time and dedication to caring for them that they have bloomed at their utmost best. And the scents," he breathed deeply, "Beautiful! My wife and I used to love coming here just for these flowers. He has managed to get blooms almost every month of the year, more than any other person I know. I think he must be a floral genius!"

Katie sat down, took in the wonderful view and savoured the sweet perfume in the air. "How does he do it?" she asked.

"He studied hard, learned from others, and practiced his craft daily so that he really understood what he was doing and how to get the best out of each variety," said Mr Smith, "But even more importantly than that, he loved what he was doing, and he did it with love."

Katie nodded appreciatively, "It shows. But it's a shame that we have to wait until we retire before we have time to do what we enjoy."

"Who says we do?"

"Well, that's just what happens isn't it? Mind you, it's only those who can afford it that actually enjoy retirement. The way things are going at the moment, I'll probably have to work until I croak!"

"Has that Negative elf been talking too loud again?"

Katie sank back against the bench, "I suppose he has, but he does have a point."

"He only has a point if you listen to him. And if you find yourself listening to him, you have to do something about it, otherwise he will suck you down into his pit of despair! You don't want that, Katie. Anyway, you looked excited when you arrived. What's been happening?"

She held up her packed lunch made at home that morning. "I hope you're proud of me. I make my own lunch now, and for Abi and Tom. It's so much cheaper. I've worked out how much I am saving by not buying coffee and lunch from the deli and paying for the kids' school lunches, and I'm putting it in a jar so I can see just how much it is. It soon adds up!"

"It will do, and I am very proud of you. But far more important than that is, Katie, are YOU proud of you?"

She frowned, before answering, "Yes, I think I am. To know that I am actively doing something for myself about my situation, actually makes me feel like I am in control of my life, rather than letting it control me."

"That is exactly the point," replied Mr Smith. "So many people allow life to happen to them without really thinking about how they can influence what happens. And then they blame everyone and everything if it doesn't turn out the way they want." He moved to reveal the inscription on this bench.

Katie read it aloud: " 'Take responsibility for you.' " She thought about it for a moment. "I thought I did already."

"I'm sure you do in a lot of ways, but you just said that you expect to have to work till you croak. Why is that?"

"Because I don't have a pension, and the state pension is barely enough to live on now, never mind in 25 years when they'll have whittled away at it even more. Who knows? It may even have disappeared by the time I retire! So for people like me, the only option will be to keep working."

"Would you be happy to let the state look after you and decide how much money you get in your old age?"

"Well no...," said Katie.

Mr Smith continued, "And who are these 'people like you', with only one option? When I look around, all I see is individuals, each with their own minds who can make their own choices about their future. None of us has to do anything we don't want to, if we choose not to. Of course we can feel trapped in our situation, but the only person who can change it is ourselves. People are presented with opportunities to change all the time, but many are either too absorbed in their current life that they don't see them, or are simply too afraid of change to take the opportunity before them."

"OK, I understand that, but it's not always as simple as that. How do we know what to do to change or how to spot a life-changing opportunity?"

"That's a fair point. What do you think? What do you normally do if you don't know how to do something, say like fix a tap, or repair the car?"

"Well, I either learn how to do it myself, or pay someone else to do it."

"Exactly. And by doing that, you take responsibility for doing something about it. It's funny how we know how to solve small practical problems like those, but we don't approach life the same way. That is, if something's not right, it's up to us to find a way to fix it because no-one will fix it for us."

Katie sighed, "I know you are right, but I'm not so sure that fixing life is so easy."

"Now I didn't say it was easy, but it is straightforward. And the best way to start is by reading."

"I'm not much of a reader. I only read on holiday. It's my treat when I go away."

"So what do you do in your spare time?"

"Well once I've finished any chores, and made sure the kids have done their homework and are ready for school the next day, I relax and watch TV."

"And how long do you do that?"

"Probably from about 7.30 to 10.30 most nights. That sounds like a lot when I think about it, doesn't it?"

"I do wonder if what you see on the TV is helping you to build a life of financial freedom for you and your family?"

"Of course it isn't, it's just a way to wind down after a hard day."

"That's understandable. But you might like to know that nearly every billionaire in the world spends at least half an hour a day reading books by other hugely successful people. They do it to learn, and they never, ever stop learning. Many credit it as the single daily habit they use that has made the difference from them being poor to being rich and successful."

"Wow. That's amazing. Just half an hour a day?"

"Or 10 pages of a good book that teaches you how to make your life better. There are so many out there – The Secret, by Rhondda Byrne, Rich Dad Poor Dad by Robert Kyosaki, Twelve Pillars by Chris Widener and Jim Rohn, The Richest man in Babylon by Charles Conrad, The Slight Edge by Jeff Olsen, The Success Principles, by Jack Canfield – I could go on. All of these people have built hugely successful lives and have written books telling the rest of us how to do it. It's all out there."

"I could do that, read for half an hour a day. I wouldn't mind giving up a bit of TV if it means I can learn how to turn my life around."

"Now that's what I like to hear, your Positive elf talking! Anyway, tell me about the rest of your week."

"Well, amazingly, that lady we met in the park last time, you remember, the one with the lovely springer, Hamish? She's called Liz, and she's offered me £20 an hour, which is amazing, for two hours a week. It's great, it's like she's paying me to do something I would love doing anyway..."

"Well fancy that," said Mr Smith with a knowing smile, "And yet, just a minute ago you were asking me how to spot a life-changing opportunity when you've only gone and done it already!"

"I'd hardly call it life-changing!," she laughed, "It's just a bit of extra pocket money, really."

Mr Smith raised an eyebrow in a way Katie had seen before. "Oh, I know what you're thinking!" she said defensively, "But there's no way I'll ever earn enough to give up my job."

"No way, eh?" Mr Smith chuckled to himself, "We'll see."

Katie continued, "It's a nice little extra, and I'll put the money away so that I don't even notice I have it."

"Good idea. When is your first session?"

"Later this week. I can't wait!"

"Have you ever noticed something about this park, Katie?"

"What, apart from how lovely it is?"

"How many people are there with dogs?"

Katie looked around, and yes, there were plenty of dogs in the park.

"And what did Liz say last week? That there was no-one round here who did dog training?"

"I'm sure there must be..."

"Well if there is, I'm sure Liz would have found them, and perhaps she did, but they were not good enough or didn't get on with her dog. Anyway, I would remember that if I were you. And if I leave you with one phrase today it is this: To be truly happy, you have to work out what it is you love doing, then find a way to make money doing it."

Katie smiled, "And take responsibility for you."

"Precisely."

Bench Five

Know your destination before the route

It was a couple of weeks before Katie saw Mr Smith again. She'd been to the park and looked out for him, but he'd not been there. She missed him when he wasn't around because she was so grateful for the few things that he had taught her that were already starting to make a difference, and she was eager to learn more.

She was loving training Liz's dog Hamish. It reminded her how much she enjoyed being around dogs and how natural the instinct to train them felt to her. Working with dogs had been a fundamental part of her life growing up and she'd almost forgotten that. And then there was the money! Not only was she earning a bit extra, she was actively looking for more ways to spend less. As Mr Smith had suggested, she'd gone through her direct debits and found gaming subscriptions the children no longer used, a monthly payment going out for a mobile phone Abi had lost two years ago, plus she'd cancelled the gym membership that until now, she had left running because she knew she ought to go, even though she hardly ever did. The gym cost her £40 a month and she'd worked out that over the past six months, she'd used it eight times, which meant it actually cost her a whopping £30 a session for the privilege of doing something she hated! What a waste of money! Now that she was training Hamish two hours a week, she got exercise through doing something she loved, she'd also started using the stairs at work, and walking instead of taking the car when she could – less expense on fuel and more exercise for her. Double the benefit!

All the extra money went into a savings account which she decided she would forget about and then it would come in useful for something one day. She had also stopped watching one TV soap and used the time instead to read one of the books Mr Smith had suggested. The thing is, she enjoyed it so much, she found herself reading more, and soon a second soap bit the dust.

She'd also taken on board what Mr Smith had said about learning your trade, and found an excellent book on the latest thinking on training dogs. She wanted to make sure she gave Liz and Hamish the best service she could and although a lot of what she knew came from her instinct and her previous experience, she wanted to get even better.

A sense of purpose had entered her life. She no longer felt trapped in a spiral of mounting debts, despair and acceptance. She still didn't enjoy her job, but because she knew she was making fundamental changes in her life, she didn't hate it quite so much. It didn't go unnoticed by her kids either. Tom had said the other day while she was making their sandwiches in the morning: "Mum, you're singing! You never sing! Is it because you're happy now?"

His words had struck a chord with her, because she had not before appreciated how her hopelessness was affecting the children. She now understood that they could see she was unhappy, but had kept it to themselves, no doubt for fear of upsetting her even more. "Yes, Tom, I am, and we are going to be a much happier family from now on!" and as she'd said it, she wished everyone could have a Mr Smith in their lives so the world would be a much happier place all round!

When she finally met Mr Smith again, he was on a new bench overlooking an ornamental maze made of chest-high box hedges. At its centre was flag on a very tall pole with the words 'FIND ME' written on it, but if you stood in the maze, it was impossible to tell which was the right way to go. Katie couldn't wait to tell Mr Smith of the progress she'd been making, but he indicated the maze before she could open her mouth.

"I love a good maze," he said, "Knowing you have to get to the centre, but not knowing the way, racing to find it before anyone else, hoping not to get lost and disorientated, running around and trying to figure out the route. It's excellent fun."

"I'm not sure everyone shares your enthusiasm, Mr Smith," said Katie as she watched a mother and daughter approach the entrance, look doubtfully in, then turn away again.

"Some people are afraid to go in for fear of getting lost and not finding the way out," smiled Mr Smith, "And then you see people like those girls and boys, who just plunged in regardless and are exhausting themselves mindlessly running here, there and everywhere in the hope that somehow they'll end up in the middle."

"They're hilarious! Look, he's just given up!" One of the boys threw his hands up as he found himself back where he started. He stomped out of the maze, and sat on the grass to await his friends.

"He's had enough, poor fellow. Before you arrived, though, I saw another young woman, all by herself, carefully making her way round," said Mr Smith. "She came across several dead ends and took numerous wrong turns, but even though she went wrong, she never became disheartened and gave up. Instead, she took time to remember her route, and which were the misleading paths. She made it to the middle eventually, and the joy of the achievement on her face was glorious to see!"

"Well, she sounds like a very wise young woman, then."

"I think she was. Now then, how have you been, Katie?"

A huge grin lit up Katie's face as she began to tell Mr Smith all about the past couple of weeks.

"I'm sorry," she said after she finally stopped talking, "I've just babbled on for ages!"

Mr Smith laughed: "Don't apologise! It's wonderful to see you so enthusiastic about what you are doing. You're a changed woman who now understands how small changes can add up to make a big difference, and even more importantly than that, you are doing something about it. There are plenty of people in the world who know all this, and yet they do nothing to change. It never ceases to amaze me."

"I just needed someone to tell me what to do, so thank you, Mr Smith. I am so grateful to you."

"Don't thank me, my dear, it's you who is doing the hard work, not me! And I haven't told you what to do at all. All I've done is helped you open your eyes so that you can see what's out there and help yourself."

He went on, "So now you've done all that, what next?"

"Next? Well, I don't know. I hadn't thought about it. More lessons with Hamish, I suppose."

"You suppose? And what happens once Hamish has finished his training?"

Katie shrugged, and Mr Smith tapped the back of the bench. She read the inscription: " 'Know your destination before the route'. Hmmm, I think I get this one. You have to know where you are going before you work out how to get there."

"Exactly. You wouldn't get in car and just set off driving without knowing your destination first, because how would you ever know which way to go? And so it is with life. So where are you going Katie? What is your destination?"

"I've not really thought about that to be honest. I just know I want to make a better life for me and the kids."

"So what is a better life for you and your children?"

"Not having to worry about money."

"Yes..."

"More happiness."

"Less work?"

"Definitely!"

"I'm sorry Katie, but that all sounds a bit wishy washy to me. You see, to really understand where you are going, you have to know exactly where you want to end up. So you have to get that absolutely clear in your mind. What does happiness actually mean to you? What do you mean by no worries about money? How much money will that take?

A few pounds? A million pounds? What? Everyone has different ideas about what they want, so you need to be very clear."

"Gosh, I don't know. I've not dared to think about it because the kind of life I want is the stuff dreams are made of."

"So dream! I dare you! Go on, tell me about your dream!"

Katie pulled a face, afraid he would think her stupid and greedy if she admitted dreaming about living a life of luxury in a world where money was no object.

"Katie, what harm will it do to speak your dreams out loud? The fear of being ridiculed, of being over-ambitious, of failing to achieve what we proclaim is what stops many people in their tracks. And for what? It's back to what I said before – what anyone thinks of me is none of my business. So don't let what anyone else thinks – and more importantly, don't let yourself think – that having dreams is anything but essential. Once you know what your dream life is, once you can picture it very clearly in your mind, then you have identified your destination and you can then begin to work out the route to get there."

Katie, smiled, and felt like a naughty child about to embark on a forbidden adventure. "OK, here goes. This is going to sound ridiculous but…"

Mr Smith held up his hand to stop her.

"Oh yes, right," said Katie, "Who cares if it sounds ridiculous? This is my dream, and what anyone else thinks doesn't matter!"

Mr Smith smiled and nodded for her to carry on.

"I am living in a beautiful house that I have bought and done up myself. If has all the mod cons, like sensory lighting, hidden speakers and beautiful stone tiles on the floor with underfloor heating that feels so good to walk on in my bare feet. All the fittings and appliances are the best quality, because I believe in paying for quality. The furnishings are in subtle neutral shades of whites, creams and golds in luxurious hand-made fabrics. The kitchen is warm, spacious and simply stunning. It's the heart of the home, where we all come together to eat and relax. Everything works seamlessly and the house is spotless, thanks to my fabulous cleaner who comes in twice a week. There is ample space for the children, who each have rooms with ensuite bathrooms. My bedroom is my sanctuary, with its own dressing room and ensuite bathroom with a gorgeous waterfall shower. Oh my goodness, now I've started, I can't stop..."

"Keep going."

"The house has a perfect and tranquil garden, which is gorgeous with lots of flowering shrubs, but without being too manicured – a kind of natural, higgledy-piggledy look - and it has a lovely terrace, which is a sun trap, where we sit on balmy summer evenings and drink chilled white wine over a barbecue."

"It sounds idyllic. And what about life outside of the home?"

"Well, I will have earned enough money to never have to work again, but because I love what I do, I still have a hand in, and of course, I enjoy every moment. I've always wanted to help worthwhile causes, so I have two charitable projects that I regularly donate to and also help out in other ways too. I imagine one charity will be to do with dogs, and another probably to do with helping young people who are struggling in life. I also have enough money to put my children on the property ladder so that they have a great start in their adult lives. On top of that,

I have a wide circle of friends and we spend lots of time together, either eating out, or coming round to mine for dinner. I also have enough money to be able to travel whenever and wherever I want, and regularly to our lovely villa in Mallorca. I am fulfilled and content and exactly where I want to be, enjoying the life I had always dreamed of." Katie smiled almost triumphantly, and Mr Smith laughed.

"Now that is more like it. And just look at your face, you are beaming! How hard was that? And how does it make you feel?"

"It feels amazing! And now I've said it out loud, I'm thinking 'Why shouldn't I dream? Where's the harm?"

"But one of the most important things is to remember how it makes you feel, and to believe with absolute certainty that it will be yours, Katie. That is not as easy once you get sucked into the everyday activities of day-to-day living. So it helps to think about your vision for a few minutes each day, picture it clearly, remember how it makes you feel and hold on to that feeling. If you make it a daily habit first thing in the morning, as regular as brushing your teeth, those feelings won't leave you."

Katie nodded: "Well that doesn't sound too hard."

"It's not, but being persistent even when you don't feel like it, that's what stops most people. So you have an idea about your destination, although I do suggest you go home and really work on it, be more specific about the details of the life you want such as the income you want. And after that, you need to do the hard bit – work out how you are going to get there."

Katie's face dropped. "How on earth am I going to do that? Where do I start?"

"What's your aim with training Hamish?"

Katie was slightly taken aback by the sudden change of subject. "Hamish? My aim is to make him a well-rounded and well behaved dog who does exactly what his owner tells him."

"And how are you going to achieve that?"

"Well I have a particular behaviour for each lesson that I want Hamish to achieve, and Liz to understand how to reinforce it at home, and I plan all the tasks that I want to do in that lesson to achieve that goal."

"So you have a goal each week, then work out what steps you need to take to achieve that goal, right? And when you have achieved all your goals, you have a fully-trained dog. And do you just make up those goals as you go along?"

"Oh no, I have them all set out for each week, and then under each week I plan a new lesson that's aimed specifically with that behaviour in mind. You have to, otherwise you'd never know where you were. I also check his progress. Sometimes he's not ready to move on to the next stage, or has a bit of a relapse, so we just go back and work on the previous behaviour a bit longer until he cracks it."

"So, you know your destination, and have worked out the steps you need to get there. Then you've broken down each of those steps into to smaller steps which make it more manageable. And if you go wrong, you work out where you are going wrong, and try again to get it right? And you've written it all down?"

Katie smiled in recognition. "I have. So you're saying I need to apply that to my life."

"To get that beautiful house and the beautiful life you have just described to me, that's exactly what you have to do. And did you know that people who plan and write down their goals are far more likely to achieve them? I told you it was straightforward!" He added: "So the lesson is, know your destination, then work out your route. Once you know your route, then plan the smaller steps you need to take for each stage of that route. And put it all in writing. So Katie, you have made an excellent start, and taken that first step, but if you stop there, will it take you all the way to that dream?"

Katie shook her head.

"And do you really want that dream, or would just a few extra quid in the bank actually make you happy?"

She shook her head again. "No, I want the dream!"

"Well then, I think you know what you have to do."

"I certainly do!"

Bench Six

You don't get rich working for someone else

Several weeks had passed since Katie had last seen Mr Smith. She still came to the park most days, and she just accepted that sometimes she would see him, and sometimes not, and these days, she saw him less often. She had worked out that they were making their way almost in a circle around the park one bench at a time, and it was always the next bench along that she would find him when he showed up. She resisted the temptation to run around reading all the inscriptions on them. She liked waiting until Mr Smith was with her, as he put so much meaning into each and every one. It was funny how he always turned up just when she needed him – not that she realised it before she'd seen him, but afterwards she found herself thinking on each occasion that his advice had come just at the right time.

The sixth bench upon which Katie met Mr Smith was the furthest she had had to walk from the entrance gate and was at the top of a steep climb. She enjoyed seeing the park from a different perspective each time and had really begun to appreciate the value in not staying in the same place.

"Oh, we can see the pond down there and there's Joe's flower garden," she said.

"Yes, and the roses are coming out now. They are my favourites because my wife loved them so. And if you look over those trees, Katie, you can also see the tops of the town centre buildings, and there's the cathedral, and if you look really hard past the cathedral tower..."

"Oh yes! I can just about see the mountains in the distance. I had no idea that this view even existed! Gosh, how far away are they?"

"A day by foot, an hour by car and less than a minute by plane. Depends how you choose to travel!"

Katie laughed, "When you put it like that, I suppose the number of miles doesn't matter, it's how long you want to spend travelling."

"That's right. But even more important than that is deciding to set off in the first place."

"You have a point!"

"So tell me what's been happening with you Katie? It's been a while since we last met."

"I have been so busy! Training with Hamish is nearly complete and has gone brilliantly - Liz is delighted. In fact, she has passed my name on to a number of her friends, several of whom have been in touch, so I am looking at when I can fit them in. I might have to think about working weekends. But I'm also thinking of setting up classes, as then I can train a few dogs at a time. Still, I do like the one to one contact with the dog as you can really build up a relationship with them, so I'm in two minds about that."

"It all sounds very promising. Your dog training seems to be taking off."

"It really is, and there is such demand for it around here. When

I'm out and about I often get chatting to people with dogs, I can't help stopping to pet nearly every one. It makes up for not having one of my own. There's been a few times when they've talked about their dogs' naughty habits, and I know I could help, but I daren't say anything."

"Why ever not?"

"Because if they asked me to take them on, I couldn't say yes because I just don't have the capacity to do it. With working full-time, spending time with the kids, and the clients I'm about to take on, I couldn't do it without compromising the quality of service I'd be able to give to people. And I won't do that."

"You're beginning to sound like a businesswoman!"

Katie nearly choked on her sandwich. "What? Are you kidding? I'm just training a few dogs in my spare time, that's all, but even so, I still like to do the best job I can. It doesn't make me a businesswoman!"

"You are beginning to think like one though. It sounds like there's a gap in the market, and it sounds like you're the one to fill it."

Katie sighed, "I still can't afford to give up work though. It's a steady, solid income that comes in every month, without fail."

"And does that monthly income get you any nearer to that dream you told me about last time?"

Katie shook her head.

"And will a couple of extra customers get you that luxury house?"

She shook her head again, and Mr Smith moved to the side to reveal the full inscription on the bench.

" 'You don't get rich working for someone else', " read Katie, before falling silent.

Mr Smith scrutinised her expression. "Thoughts, Katie?"

"I guess deep down, I did know that, but I just don't know if I would have the courage to give up my job."

"Have you been working on your route plan that we talked about last time?"

"I have. And I seem to be very good at the big steps or goals, but working out the detail is tricky."

"Is it tricky? Or is it more that to get where you want to go, you are going to have to make some difficult decisions and choices that you didn't want to confront?"

"Such as give up work? But it just seems so risky."

"What do you risk by staying put? The cost of living rising faster than salaries, little extra to save and invest for the future, and a stagnated working life in a job you don't enjoy! That sounds far more risky to me! A friend, who is a multi-millionaire, described it like this: You are walking towards the top of a cliff and have to make the decision to either jump off, or to turn round and walk back from the edge. What would you do?"

"Keep away! I don't have a death wish!"

"And that's what most people would do and which is why they are not wealthy. But what you should do is go right to the edge of the cliff and look over. Until you do, you have no idea what lies on the other side. There might be a sheer drop to certain death, but on the other hand, there might be a soft landing, or there might be trees to climb down, or there might be safe ledges all the way down. The thing is, you will never know what is on the other side until you've had a look over the edge. It's the same approach to making a decision that involves risk.

You have to weigh up all the consequences of jumping off that cliff, right down to the worst case scenario. And if you can live with the worst case scenario, then you should jump."

Katie stared towards the mountains in the distance as she pondered Mr Smith's words.

He continued: "But you wouldn't blindly jump off the cliff, plummet to the bottom and just hope you wouldn't die, would you? That would be crazy. You would look for safe ways to get to the bottom, ways to make it easier. In your case, for example, you don't have to give up working completely right away, but perhaps ask if you could drop a day? Would that be a more manageable first step?"

It was like a light had switched on in Katie's eyes. "And then I would have the time time to see more clients and earn the money I've given up but by doing something I love! Of course! Why didn't I think of that? I was just focussing on giving up work completely, focussing on jumping without looking. It's like you said, think of the goal, then break it down into smaller, more manageable steps."

"But never lose sight of the bigger goals that lead towards the ultimate dream. Keep asking yourself: 'Is what I am doing taking me closer to my dream?' If it is, keep going, if it isn't, change direction and find another route."

"I tell you what, Mr Smith, I am damn well going into work tomorrow and the first thing I am going to do is ask to reduce my hours."

"Good for you! Katie, you are on your way!"

Treasure your daily Golden Hour

Katie was finding that the weeks were flying by. She was busier than ever, but enjoying every day as she knew she was working towards the life she dreamed for herself and the children.

She had been nervous approaching her boss about reducing her hours, but once she explained why, she was amazed at her reaction: "That sounds fantastic Katie, and if I could I would do something like that too. Between you and me – and this is not to go beyond these four walls – things are going to get very tough in here soon. The directors are looking for ways to reduce costs, so you cutting your hours is actually doing me a favour. Times are hard, and people here are soon going feel it."

It made Katie realise that actually she had no choice BUT to strike out on her own and build her business. Her business! It was the first time she had actually referred to it as that. It WAS a business, and not just some spare-time hobby, and it was about time she started treating it as such.

She would have to find it a name, maybe get some cards printed. Advertise? But at the moment, she had enough clients to fill the extra day, so what should she next do? All these thoughts were whirling round her head as she sat on the seventh bench and watched a teacher with a group of primary school children carrying clipboards walking on the patch of grass in front of her, noting down the types of plants and insects that they spotted. She hadn't noticed Mr Smith approaching.

"You beat me to it today, Katie!"

"Oh hello Mr Smith! I did. I had a feeling you'd come today, so I guessed that it would be this bench."

"So you've worked me out then!"

"Well I have worked out that we are gradually working our way round the benches in this park, and that we are on number seven."

"Well spotted," said Mr Smith as he sat down. "And you know, I never get bored of what I see from each and every bench. I think I see and learn something new every single time."

"Even now? After all these years, you are still learning?"

"Thank you for reminding me of my advanced status," he laughed, "But yes, I never stop looking for things to notice, and never stop learning from the world around me. Nor should we ever. School is one way to learn," he said, nodding towards the children, "But for me, you cannot find a better teacher than life."

"That's true," agreed Katie, "But I think you've taught me more than anyone or anything I've ever come across. If only they had people like you in our schools. What I have learned from you is so valuable! Surely if we start educating our young ones earlier in life, we would all be in a better place? If I had been taught what you have taught me 20 years ago, I would have been financially secure by now, I'm sure of it!"

"I think you are right. It's never too young to start learning the essential skills to financial freedom."

"It's true," said Katie, "Young ones are like sponges, they just soak up information without prejudging it. If it was up to me, I'd rip up the curriculum and start again."

"Hear, hear! Katie for Prime Minister!"

"Ha haaa! That's one job I'd not want. In fact, I don't think I want any job! I want to work for myself for evermore."

"Now someone has changed their tune since last time we spoke! What's been happening?"

"I am loving my 'dog day' as I call it. I have private clients during the day, then an evening class which is better for those who work nine to five. The thing is, although I love it, it is sooo busy! I work all day, then fix the kids' tea, help them with homework if needed, make sure they are all set for school the next day, then when the babysitter arrives, I rush out to the class. The great thing, though, is that I can do it here in the park, which is free. It would be good to have somewhere that is covered when the weather gets bad. If it's dreadful, I have to cancel the class, which I don't like doing as I hate to let people down."

"And as a businesswoman, you hate to lose money! At least that should be in your mind too."

"Yes, it is, I just don't want to sound greedy."

Mr Smith laughed loudly, "You will not find any serious business person afraid to admit that the money coming in and going out is uppermost in their minds! But as you know, you are still learning, and I know that it won't take long for your business brain to fully develop.

You sound incredibly busy."

"I am, and I'm so busy answering emails and phone calls, doing paperwork, working out training plans for each dog and their owner, and developing new training techniques after work each day and at weekends, and that's before all the domestic stuff like cleaning, washing, shopping, and the children's after-school activities and the like. I just don't seem to have the time to do much else."

"So how much time do you set aside each day to work on your business?"

"Like I said, I do most of it on my dog day, and the rest in my spare time."

"That's not what I meant – what you have described is you working IN your business. I want to know when you work ON your business. The time you devote to planning for your future growth, assessing and reassessing your steps to your goals and focussing on your dream so you know that what you are doing is taking you there."

"I know what you're saying, and it is important, but I just don't have the time right now..."

"It is not simply important, Katie, it is vital." And Mr Smith pointed to the next inscription, which Katie read out.

" 'Treasure your daily Golden Hour.'"

"That's right. It is the one most important thing you should do each and every single day if you are serious about reaching your goals. How many people do you know who, when asked 'How's work?' always say 'I'm so busy, I never stop!' And yet, how many of those people are actually really productive?"

Katie thought about her work colleagues and many of her friends who always seemed to be rushed off their feet, but she wasn't really sure why they were so busy. "Yes, but that's life isn't it, life is busy and we just have to wade on through it. But now you're going to tell me I'm wrong, aren't you? I can tell!"

Mr Smith chuckled. "If that's how you want to carry on, then go on. For many people, feeling busy makes them feel better. But if it were me, I'd rather be less busy, but more productive, and your Golden Hour is the key to that. It sets your mind up for the day ahead, and your mind is the key to your future success.

"One of my favourite quotes comes from the legendary US basketball coach John Wooden, who said: 'Never mistake activity for achievement'. And that's what you have to do. Don't be happy because you are busy, be happy because you have accomplished something, because every time you do, you will be a little closer to your goals."

Mr Smith went on to explain the key elements of the Golden Hour.

"People can choose how to use the hour, but the most important thing is that it is devoted to working on your business, not in your business, and that it is a sacrosanct daily habit. This is what I do in my Golden Hour. There are three main elements to my hour: Gratitude, affirmations and working on my future goals."

Mr Smith observed the expression in Katie's eyes, and laughed. "Just because I'm an old man doesn't mean I don't still have goals for the future, Katie."

She grinned sheepishly, and he continued, "My gratitude and affirmations take about 20 minutes, and the rest of the time I devote to thinking about my future, refining my steps and goals. This hour is sacrosanct to me, and should be for you too – no interruptions, no checking emails or phones. It might mean getting up earlier in the day, or, while you have your job, it could mean splitting it in half, so you do some in the morning and some in the evening, but the main thing is you have to do it each and every day without fail."

"What do you mean by gratitude?"

"Start the day by thinking about two or three things in your life you are grateful for. It could be something that has happened in the previous 24 hours, like an act of kindness someone has bestowed upon you, or it could be something general, like gratitude for your children, or for the flowers you see in this park. Anything you choose, and write them down. Keep a journal or a gratitude list, and then you can also go back and read them whenever you want to. Have your list next to your bed, and do it as soon as you wake up and you will start the day with a ready-to-go positive mindset."

"Ok. That sounds simple enough. So what are affirmations?" asked Katie.

"Affirmations are where you say, preferably out loud, a statement about your future goals and dreams, and you say it in the present tense, as if it is true already. You remember when you told me about your dream of living in a beautiful house? You may not have realised that you said it all in the present tense – it was a like a long affirmation. An affirmation can be anything, and it has to be in positive language too. For example, instead of saying: 'I'm not living in the shadow of debt' say: 'I am living an abundant and wealthy life'. Choose two or three a day, and as you say them, visualise it happening in your mind and allow the feelings it invokes to engulf you. It is not always as easy as it sounds, but if you keep doing it, you will get better at it. You can choose to do the same ones each day, or different ones each time. What I do is two relating to my future goals, and one relating to the coming day. I also write them down as that helps me to visualise."

Katie pulled a face: "So you do all this? It all sounds very – what's the word – whacky! Does it actually work?"

"I know several extremely intelligent and successful entrepreneurs who swear by it."

"And what about you? Do you swear by it?"

Mr Smith looked directly at Katie. "I have always lived by it! The mind is your most powerful asset, and it does not know the difference between reality and dreams. But it does understand feelings, negative and positive, and reacts accordingly. Create positive images and feelings and you will attract the same into your life as your mind influences the Universe. It's called the Law of Attraction."

"I've heard of that," said Katie.

"I suggest you read up on it. The Secret is probably the most famous book about it, but there are many more.

"Now, the last bit is less spiritual and more practical. As I said, I use mine to work on and define the steps towards my goals, and to assess whether I'm going in the right direction. But you, perhaps, could spend the rest of your hour working on your business by developing business strategy, mapping out business priorities, learning and development, and for defining what you need to do to move you ever closer to achieving your goals. Add these three things together and you will find it becomes the most powerful and productive part of your day."

"Well if it's good enough for multimillionaires, then maybe I should give it a go!" said Katie.

Mr Smith laughed. "It will be easier once you have given up your job – which will happen – as then you can factor it in to your working day. One last tip that a busy woman like you could benefit from: On Sunday, spend half an hour prioritising the tasks for the week ahead. You will then know exactly what you have to do and because of that, the thought of all the things you need to do the coming week won't be weighing on your mind, which will mean you will be more rested, less stressed and more productive during that week."

Katie looked Mr Smith earnestly in the eyes: 'Thank you for everything you are doing for me. You have literally changed my life, and I know it is only going to get better."

"Well, you can put me on your gratitude list tomorrow morning then!"

"Oh I will!" said Katie.

Bench Eight

Make your money work for you

It was a good few weeks before Katie saw Mr Smith again and although she was still very busy, she had implemented a golden hour every day, making it more manageable by splitting it into two as Mr Smith had suggested.

She was amazed at what a difference making a gratitude list had made to her mindset. She had stopped waking in the morning with that horrible feeling of dread for having to go to work, of feeling trapped on a never-ending hamster wheel. Now, not only did it make her start the day feeling positive, it really made her pay attention to all the good she already had in her life so that she appreciated just how much she had to be grateful for. She mentally took note every time she came across something she wanted to express thanks for so that she could add it to her gratitude list, and also said a quick 'thank you' in her mind there and then. Just a few weeks ago, she wouldn't have paid much attention to the way someone helped her in a shop, or when a journey was traffic jam free, or for the fact that her children always remembered their pleases and thank yous. But it was as if until now she had been drifting through an endless fog while these simple but meaningful daily pleasures passed her by unnoticed. But now, the fog had lifted and she was looking at life and the world around her with a new clarity of vision, habitually focussing on the good stuff, rather than the bad. In fact, she barely ever heard her negative elf these days!

She had said her affirmations out loud every morning and found that the more she said them, the clearer she was able to visualise the dream house she had described to Mr Smith. Seeing the picture in her mind every day also strengthened her resolve to achieve it so that it was not difficult for her to maintain her focus on building her business. Thanks to her Golden Hour, she had built up a clear strategy for growth that she was eager to share with Mr Smith when she found him as expected on the eighth bench.

"Have you noticed," he began, "How well those delphiniums are blooming compared to those just over there which seem smaller and less robust?"

"Oh yes, I wonder why? Perhaps they don't get as much sun, or the ground isn't as fertile."

"I think you might be right there, Katie. Plants always fare better if they have the right conditions to flourish in. Even though they are not far away from each other, there is a marked difference."

"I'm sure Joe would know. He's the expert."

"He definitely would. I will ask him when I next see him. Now my dear, what have you got to tell me this time?"

"So much! I believe that the potential for growth around here is huge, so I want to find people I can work with so that I can take on more dogs. I use part of my Golden Hour to research ways of growing, and marketing, and I'm investigating ways of being able to deliver training to a lot of people, without actually having to do it myself. So for example, online tutorials that people can watch as and when they want, and step-by-step programmes that they can buy or subscribe to. I'm also thinking of having some kind of discussion forum. I'm looking at a name like 'Dogsnet' or something. They have these kinds of websites for parents, so I'm thinking there's space for one about dogs too as nine million households in this country have one. Anyone who owns a dog knows it can be like having another child at times! Anyway, it means I can reach a much wider audience which doesn't necessarily have to be local. I'm also planning to film training sessions and upload them to my website, which is being developed now, so that local clients can re-watch their own dog in training and remind themselves what they need to do at home themselves. My job is as much about educating them as it is about schooling the dog. Online is the way to go, I think, to create a growing business. Just training a few dogs each week will not get me that house and life so I have to think much bigger, but I'm very clear about what steps I need to take to move forward and I've worked out an exit strategy and timescale for leaving work completely. That Golden Hour has been a revelation!"

Mr Smith beamed at her: "Katie, you have blown me away! You are so focussed, and there's a determination in your voice that I haven't heard before. I am so impressed!"

"But it is all thanks to you."

"All I've done is help you expand your horizons and understand how much potential you – and every single one of us – have inside. Most people just do not realise it. Now you do, and you are doing all the hard work that it takes to achieve your dreams.

"Now, Katie, let's cut to the nitty gritty. Are you earning more money now?"

"Oh yes! I see four or five dogs for one to ones on my dog day, which brings in £240 to £300 a day, then a class of six dogs in the evening, which brings in around £70 a time. It means I take home between around £800 to £1000 extra a month after my costs! It's amazing."

"And what are you doing with that extra money?"

"I'm being very sensible! No more reckless shopping sprees. I pay off an extra £100 on my credit card, which I no longer use, so that debt is steadily reducing, I set aside a certain amount per month dedicated to running and growing the business, and the rest I put in my savings account."

"That sounds fairly sensible. And what rate of interest are you getting on your savings?"

Katie pulled a face: "I'm not sure exactly. Not very much I suspect because I know interest rates are very low right now. But at least I know it's safe and I won't be too tempted to spend it."

"You might want to change your opinion about what keeping money 'safe' means," said Mr Smith, before pointing to the inscription on the bench.

" 'Make your money work for you'," read Katie.

"You're right that interest rates are very low at the moment, but have you thought about inflation? You know, the cost of living?"

Katie shook her head, "Not really, it's low too but I don't know how low."

"Inflation is at 0% as we speak, but that won't last, and at some point it will start to climb, as it always does eventually. And you can bet your bottom dollar that, over the long term, inflation will rise more quickly than the interest on your savings. You said you plan to leave your money there and forget about it, but do you know that if you do that, it will actually lose value in real terms in the long run?"

"I hadn't thought about it like that. I just thought it was the best place for it."

"Many people make that mistake. And they also don't consider that it won't be protected from tax. For example, if, god forbid, you die suddenly, that money will be subject to inheritance tax, which means your beneficiaries, which I imagine are your children, will possibly have to pay 40% tax on that money that you have worked so hard to save. It seems unfair that if you've worked hard and already paid your taxes that you have to pay yet more when you die."

"Yes, that does seem harsh. So what do I do?"

"You make your money work for you by investing."

"Investing? Me? Isn't that for people who A. have already made their money, and B. know what they're doing?"

"Investing is for anyone and everyone who is interested in making their money work for them. It's a misconception that many people believe that it's not for them. So they leave their hard-earned cash sitting in bank or building society accounts with a terrible interest rate and allow it to lose real value over the years."

"But I haven't the first idea about investing and I know it's a risky business!"

"Do you remember when I asked you what you do when you don't know how to fix a tap?"

"Yes, find someone who does."

"There you go! There are people out there who are experts in financial and tax planning, and who are desperate to help people like you grow their money, and very importantly, the industry is highly regulated after the bad practices of the past. But when it comes to trusting someone to look after your money, you need to make sure you have done your research. If possible find someone who comes personally recommended and has a proven track record. Or if there's someone you look up to, ask them where they go. It is the financial planner's job to get to know you and find out how risky you want to go, and they will find an investment that matches what you want to achieve. Obviously, investments with a low risk – and there are plenty around – will grow at a slower rate, while those that grow faster carry a greater risk, but mark my words, even the low risk savings will perform better than a cash savings account. An expert will also advise you on tax efficiency so that you do not pay more than you have to."

"There's been a lot in the news about tax lately – about avoidance... some of it sounds highly unethical," said Katie.

"Tax avoidance is perfectly legal, but tax evasion is not, as is right and proper. And there are some tax avoidance schemes that sail very close to the wind, which are the ones that make the news, but generally these are used by extremely rich people. There is nothing wrong or remotely unethical with you using perfectly legal ways to reduce your tax liability. People who do not pay attention to this sort of stuff end up just throwing money down the drain. Why would you want to do that?"

"When you put it like that, I'm now thinking I need to sort this as a matter of priority. But isn't it expensive to pay someone else? Couldn't I do it myself?"

"You could do it yourself, and many do, but is a bit like household DIY. Some people are great at it and achieve amazing results, some people pay the professionals to make sure it is done properly, and others give it a good go and end up botching it up! You have to decide what you are prepared to do. I choose to pay a professional and have gained far more than I've paid out by doing so. But whatever you decide to do, trust me when I say that every day your money is sitting in that savings account, it will be losing value in real terms once inflation starts to rise again. Now my advice would be to keep some in there that you want instant access to for big expenses like holidays, or in case of a large unexpected payment, but then the rest, move it to where it grows in real value. If you improve your understanding, then you will be in a much better position once the big bucks start rolling in!"

"Mr Smith, by following your advice I have already achieved far more than I ever thought possible, so I am going to get on this right away."

"Katie, I've grown to know you very well, and I know that what you say you are going to do, you do. You are building an amazing future for you and your family."

Bench Nine

Surround yourself with the right people

Katie was so eager to see Mr Smith that when she finally found him on bench nine in late summer, she could barely contain herself. But before she could launch into her latest progress report, Mr Smith drew her attention to the view from the bench. A beautiful rockery bursting with an array of succulents, heathers and ferns rose up from the ground just in front of them. Katie followed it round with her eyes where it led to a stream that was trickling down from a gentle incline behind the bench. The stream ran under a small bridge a little way further along the path, past the rockery, then continued its journey towards the pond, which they were now looking at from the opposite angle from when they sat on the second bench a few months ago.

"Beautiful," said Katie, "There's something so tranquil about the sound of trickling water."

"There is, isn't there?" agreed Mr Smith. "But when it rains, this stream swells, and if the rain persists, the trickle grows into a raging torrent. You can see where the water has eroded the edges. "

"Oh yes! It's hard to imagine it. It looks so serene at the moment."

"It certainly does. But don't underestimate the power of a little stream! Now, tell me about you, Katie."

"Oooo so much to say, Mr Smith! My website is up and running and I've set up a blog about my training sessions, plus a discussion forum, which is a really useful way to gain feedback from my clients - very helpful in understanding what they actually want. I've also found the ideal premises not too far away and hope to secure the lease on them to start just after I finish work."

"So do you have an official date when you leave then?"

"Yes, in fact it is exactly two months from today! And for these last couple of months, I am also down to three days, as work were looking for people to cut their hours, which was ideal for me. It means I can now take on some more dogs during the day, but also concentrate on setting up Dogsnet. When you get into it, there's an awful lot of work so the extra time is just what I need."

"And how about your finances?"

"I did a bit of digging, and also approached an old friend who I haven't spoken to in a while, but who has done exceptionally well in his business, and he was very helpful when it came to advice. It was great to catch up with him actually, even though I was nervous."

"Why were you nervous?"

"Well, he's so successful that I was really scared to get in touch as I thought he might be too busy and just too intimidating. And yet it was very far from the truth when I got to speak to him. I didn't think we'd have anything in common, but we chatted for ages and he was delighted to help."

"Well he certainly sounds like a great person to keep in touch with."

"He is, and he asked me to keep him up to date about my business, which is great. I also had a meeting with a couple of financial advisors that he suggested, and went with the one I felt I had the best rapport with. She has set up an ISA for me that is tax efficient, but low risk – I'm not ready invest in anything riskier just yet, but she suggested that maybe later, when I feel more confident, I can put a small amount into something a bit more high risk..."

"As long as you can afford it, that is the key. It's the old mantra – never risk more than you can afford to lose. It's an often repeated one, but very sound."

"Yes, that's true. And I will definitely stick to it as I am never going back to just scraping by."

"I love your attitude Katie! So how do your friends and family feel about what you're doing?"

Katie fell silent.

"Katie?"

She sighed heavily, "You know, I thought everyone would be supportive like you, you know, excited about what I was doing. But really, it's been the opposite. My parents think I'm mad for giving up a job with a regular income, even though I told them I wasn't earning enough as I was getting deeper into debt, plus the fact that work were looking at cutbacks, and it was very possible that I would have been made redundant anyway!"

"It's true, but your parents come from a generation where a 'job for life' was the norm, and you could retire on a pretty decent pension. But the world has changed dramatically since then, and that simply doesn't exist anymore, does it? And the bravest among us will strike out on our own, just like you, because we know it is the only way to have any chance of achieving our dreams."

"But my parents won't have it. And I've even been surprised by some of my closest friends, who all speak so negatively about the future. Here I am really excited about my new business and the potential, which I can see with such clarity. But all they focus on is what could go wrong."

"And what you need to keep focussing on, is what could go right!" said Mr Smith, and he tapped the back of the bench.

" 'Surround yourself with the right people', " read Katie.

"It's one of the things successful people do very well. They make sure they mix with people they want to learn from and who are as successful or even more successful than them. If you are surrounded by people who are constantly pointing out negatives and complaining about life, what will that do to you?"

"Yes, I see what you mean. But they are my friends and family…"

"Of course I'm not going to tell you to cut yourself off from your family and your closest friends, but you need to be aware of who you are taking advice from, and the cumulative effect of repeated negative comments. You need to surround yourself with and listen to those who are in a position that you aspire to be in, or who have a positive and supportive mentality. Constant exposure to criticism and negativity is like an unremitting trickle into your consciousness that can soon become a torrent which sweeps you away from your purpose."

Katie thought back to the last conversation she'd had with one of her oldest friends, one whom she loved, but who always seemed to be cross about something or other. She remembers how she felt after she'd left, and Mr Smith was right, her mood had been decidedly downbeat. And she thought of her well-meaning father, who was full of advice about her career and money, but, as much as she loved him, he'd worked in the civil service all his life until retirement. It wasn't the life she wanted for herself.

Mr Smith continued, "Your close friends and family will all offer advice based on their own upbringings, experiences and environments, and they will do it out of love and concern for you, of course. But they are not you and one thing successful people understand is that you should never take business or financial advice from someone who is not in a position you'd like to be in yourself.

"Take your successful friend – how did you feel about the advice he gave you?"

"I trusted it implicitly. And I wanted to be like him."

"Of course you did, because he is successful and would only have used someone he trusted for his financial advice. So if you suggest you meet up with him again, do you think he'd agree?"

"I'm sure he would."

"And what kind of circles do you think he mixes in?"

"I know the circles he mixes in – I'm friends with him on social media now, so I can see very well! Rich and successful ones!"

"And will they be the kinds of people whose advice you will want to listen to?"

"Very much so. I will suggest another meet up with him."

"Don't be afraid to connect with the people you know who might be helpful to you, and reach out to others you don't yet know. Work out ways you can tap into the networks of successful people. And lastly, distance yourself from those who hold you back. If you are truly intent on taking this journey, Katie, sometimes you have to make tough decisions."

Katie turned to watch the stream once more as it made its peaceful way down towards the pond.

Bench Ten

Fail. Learn. Persist. Grow.

By the time Katie saw Mr Smith again, autumn had well and truly taken hold. In the park, the leaves on the trees had turned from luscious greens to golden browns, radiant yellows and chestnutty reds, and were gradually loosening their grip on their woody hosts. The air was cooler too, and the amber sun made the whole park take on a gilt-edged glow.

"Just look at all the shades and colours, Katie, aren't they glorious? So rich – I always have to wonder at the multitude of browns, reds and golds at this time of year."

"I know. Simply stunning. It's a shame that in a few weeks, the trees will be bare."

"It's just the circle of life, Katie. They give the appearance of dying, but in truth, they are simply building and preserving strength over the barren and cold winter months, so that when the right time comes, they are ready to burst into full splendour again. And with each passing year, they grow bigger and sturdier. I've watched these trees over many years.

Some of them were barely more than twigs when I first encountered them, you'd have thought they'd have been whisked away on the first strong breeze. But would you look at them now? So strong and robust! You have no doubt that whatever winter is going to throw at them, they are going to come back stronger, year after year."

"I've never really thought about them like that before," said Katie, "You talk about them like they are people."

"Well, they are living things with a life of their own, and contribute much to our wonderful planet, so they deserve our respect. After all, they're going to be here a lot longer than us."

"That is certainly true. I sometimes wish I had their staying power," said Katie, wistfully.

"I note a different tone in your voice today, Katie, a note of doubt?"

Katie let out a long sigh. "Let's just say I have had a pretty rubbish couple of weeks. It's led me to question whether I am doing the right thing."

"Oh dear. So what has happened?"

"Where do I start?," said Katie, throwing up her hands. "The venue that I was hoping for, which would have been perfect, has fallen through at the last minute. All the plans that I had been working on, which were tailored to that venue and ready to implement as soon as we had the premises, are now all in vain. I have no venue to use and so am struggling to know what to do. Then a client's cheque bounced, another hasn't paid me for several weeks, another one-to-one client who was going to come for eight weeks cancelled, and to cap it off, one of the dogs I was training last week bit its owner in front of me, after I had supposedly cured it of that habit! It's like everything is falling in around my ears and I only have a few weeks left at work before I lose my steady income."

"Goodness! That is all very challenging!"

"I'm just beginning to question whether it's all worth it. I've been working like a...a..."

"A dog?" suggested Mr Smith.

Katie couldn't help but laugh, "Yes!" she cried with exasperation, "A damn dog! But when stuff like this happens, you realise that things can very quickly go wrong."

"And it knocks you off track, doesn't it?"

"Yes."

"But just because you've been knocked off track, it doesn't mean you have to stay off the track, does it?"

"I know, but I'm wondering after all this effort, is it worth getting back on?"

"Do you know how many times Thomas Edison was knocked off track before he discovered the light bulb?"

Katie shook her head.

"A thousand times. Think about that. A thousand times! And when he was asked what it felt like to fail a thousand times, he apparently replied: 'I didn't fail a thousand times. The light bulb was an invention with a thousand steps.' What a wonderful approach that is! Then there was Henry Ford who famously failed seven times before he found success with the Model T car, and Walt Disney was sacked from his newspaper for not being creative enough! Every successful person will tell you that difficulties and failure are an integral, and vital, part of your journey towards success. The thing that they all had in common was that they kept going, despite the knock-backs. Dealing with challenges enables you to learn how to handle them when they come along again, and believe me, they will! It's how you deal with them that matters." Mr Smith shifted to reveal the inscription.

" 'Fail. Learn. Persist. Grow', " read Katie.

"And the key is 'persist', " said Mr Smith. "Whatever happens, whatever knocks you off your path, you get up, you learn what went wrong and why, and you keep going. Do that, and you will grow and get stronger every step of the way, just like those trees. That's what Thomas Edison did, that's what Henry Ford, Walt Disney and countless others did, because they had a purpose that they believed in, and no matter what, they kept going."

"But what if you keep going, and you're heading down the wrong path?"

"That's where your route planning comes in that we talked about before. You have to keep an eye on your figures as well as an eye on your goals and regularly make sure you're heading in the right direction. Checking and assessing is all part of that process, and your planning must involve what you would do in the worst case scenario. What would be the worst thing that could go wrong? Have a strategy for that. What is the second worst thing? Have a strategy for that. By analysing what could go wrong – as well as what could go right – you remove the fear associated with failing, because you have thought of it and you have a plan ready for that situation. And because you are continually checking your progress, you will be able to spot in advance if you are going backwards and do something about it."

"Well the worst has happened. I've lost my premises."

"Is that worse than having no customers?"

"Well, no...Crikey, if I lost my customers, I'd have no business at all! It's just that I put so much effort into getting this venue, and now it's all for nothing."

"Just read the second word of that inscription again."

" 'Learn', " said Katie.

"What have you learned from the lease falling through?"

"That things can go wrong at the last minute."

"Precisely. Anything else?"

Katie frowned and thought hard for a moment. "I've learned which letting agents I trust and don't trust..erm...which ones charge the most commission...Oh! And I've learned which areas are better than others, that parking is a must - but hard to find with the right building - and I've also learned what insurance I need to have." She laughed, "Actually, I have learned quite a lot, haven't I?"

"You have. But you haven't mentioned the most important one for this particular situation."

Katie paused as she thought about it for a moment, then her eyes lit up. "I should have had a back-up venue. I just assumed everything would go swimmingly, but now it hasn't, I don't have a Plan B, which has made life even more difficult."

"That's right. Contingency planning is an essential part of every business, and now you've had some challenges, it will help you develop that plan. With each of your difficulties, you should assess why each happened, and what you can do to improve, then implement those measures to guard against it happening again. It's useful to write all this stuff down too. Going back and studying your mistakes and the lessons learned makes for great reading, for yourself and others down the line. And everything you just told me will come in extremely useful in your search for a new venue."

"I know, and you're right. It's just that I promised my clients that we'd have super-duper premises in a couple of weeks."

"So just tell them the truth. People appreciate honesty and most are very understanding. For those who make a fuss, well, you can't please everybody!"

"I suppose not."

"And don't forget your affirmations – a new one can be that you are in your new venue, full of excitement at starting your first class. Believe it and it will happen."

Katie leant back and looked out towards the beautiful autumn trees and smiled, "It will happen. I know it will."

"That's the spirit, Katie. Sometimes life can be very hard on us, and when it is, it is often easy to focus on everything that is going wrong there and then. But at those times, it is always worth looking at how far you have come. I remember the shy, unhappy woman I encountered on that first park bench where you and I met. Look at where you are now, compared to then?"

Katie chuckled as she remembered that she had at first thought Mr Smith was a dirty old man! How wrong had she been?

"When times are difficult," said Mr Smith, "it is even more important to remember everything you have learned since you started joining me on these park benches.

"On bench two, you learned to listen hard for the voice of Positive elf, because Negative always senses when you are feeling vulnerable and he will make the most of it. Don't let him find his voice again!

"You will face financial challenges along the way, but bench three taught you to always remember to pay yourself first, no matter what.

"Bench four reminded you that as long as you take responsibility for you, you will take charge of your own destiny.

"And on bench five, you learned the importance of knowing where you were going before working out how to get there.

"You accepted that the rich never get rich working for other people on bench six.

"And then on bench seven, you discovered the power of the Golden Hour, the most meaningful part of your day. Hold on to it, practice it, and it will take your further than you ever dreamed possible.

"When we got to number eight, you erased your fear of investing by understanding that you need to make your money work for you, and that you can decide the level of risk you want to take.

"Then on bench nine you accepted that to be successful, you need to surround yourself with the right people.

"And lastly, here we are on bench ten, with one of the most important lessons of all, that even though you will experience failures along the way, you will learn from your mistakes, persist in your endeavours, and grow stronger with every step."

Katie sat back to allow everything he had said sink in. "Wow!" she said eventually, "I have learned so much, Mr Smith, and what you have given me is like a blueprint for life, for success, for everything I could ever want."

"You could say that," he nodded, with a kindly smile.

"But what about bench number one? Did we miss out a lesson from bench number one?"

Mr Smith pointed to the path up ahead. "Can you see where that bench is?"

Katie realised he was pointing to the very bench where they first met. "Oh yes! We've almost come full circle! I can't wait to see what it says. Of course, I was so wrapped up in myself and my woes back then that it never occurred to me to pay any attention to the inscription on that first bench. Once we get there, we will just have to start going round again, won't we?"

Mr Smith smiled. "I am so delighted that now you appreciate what you see when you come to the park, Katie, and if I have in some way helped you in that discovery, well, then I am honoured."

"Helped me? You are THE reason I came back to this park and THE reason that I have turned my life around. I know I am having a hard time at the moment, but thanks to everything you have taught me, I know I can change it, and I will get through it. I will take everything I've learned and keep using it and keep reinforcing it because now I know that if I do these things, it will take me to that dream house and dream life. I don't know how to thank you, Mr Smith."

"You getting that dream house will be all the thanks I need, Katie!"

She laughed, "Oh, I will!" And as she said that, she heard the clock in the market square chiming the hour. "Goodness, time has flown! I must get back. Thank you again, Mr Smith, and see you next time."

"It has been nothing but a pleasure Katie. You take care."

Mr Smith watched as Katie headed with purpose up the path, towards the gate, and out of the park.

"There she goes, Mr Smith. She looks like a different person, now, doesn't she?" said Joe, who had wandered up to the bench.

"She certainly does, Joe."

"Is she ready to fly, then, do you think Mr Smith?"

"She is ready to fly, Joe."

Mr Smith stood up, and with a nod to Joe, the two elderly men pottered off, chattering happily, and savouring the sights around them as they walked.

Bench Eleven

I gave you wings, but you must fly by yourself

C hristmas had come and gone, and winter was in retreat. Buds were beginning to appear on the branches overhead, and as Katie walked into the park, all the signs were that spring was just around the corner.

So much had happened since she had last seen Mr Smith, that she could hardly believe it herself. She looked towards the first bench, and there was no sign of him, and so, as she was somewhat earlier than she would normally be, she decided to stroll around the park a while, and no doubt he would be there on her return.

She headed down the path in the direction of the second bench, her mind full of the details of the status report that she couldn't wait to deliver to Mr Smith. Her business had really taken off and the plans she had for the future were so exciting!

Since she had last seen him, she had secured a venue, which had everything she needed, and had started hosting lessons there. She had recruited and trained a number of excellent dog trainers who were now delivering her particular method of training, both as classes and one to ones, under the brand 'Netdogslive', which reflected her Netdogs website. They had more clients than ever and she had handed day to day running of the business to her head trainer which meant she had a less hands-on role, but could step in as and when needed.

Katie admired the tranquil pond as she strolled past bench two, glancing at the inscription as she did so. 'In loving memory of Barbara Cooper 1931 – 1988'. She stopped, and read again, to make sure she wasn't seeing things. But no, it definitely was a different inscription.

She reasoned that some of the park benches must have been moved around, maybe because they'd been taken away to be revarnished over the quiet winter months. She carried on walking, mulling over what she planned to tell Mr Smith.

Since she had taken on her head trainer, Katie had been able to devote more time to cultivating her online presence, which was where she saw the biggest potential for growth. Through her increasing network of contacts, she had found an excellent team of web developers who were helping her to expand and build the functionality of Netdogs, and also handled her social media presence. Each of her training videos were being viewed countless times by people all over the world, and she was about to launch a subscription service that would offer extra membership benefits which she was currently working on. On top of that, a Netdogs app was just weeks away from appearing, and she was also writing a 'how-to' dog-training guide. She had also been approached by an entrepreneurial-minded dog trainer from the other side of the country who was so impressed with her methods and her website, that he was looking to use her technique with his own clients.

They were discussing the possibility of franchising her Netdogslive brand.

In less than a year, Katie's original business had grown enormously, but she knew that if she got her online presence right, Netdogs would explode. It was only now that she felt like she was a real-life proper businesswoman!

She paused in front of Joe's flower garden, and could see that the daffodils and bluebells were not far off blooming. He really had thought of every season, had Joe. She was just about to walk on when a plaque on a pedestal near the entrance to the flower garden caught her attention. She walked over to it and read what it said.

"This flower garden is dedicated to the memory of Joe Thompson, whose hard work and devotion brought to life the beauty in this park that we all enjoy today."

"Oh no!" exclaimed Katie, not realising she was speaking out loud. She assumed Joe must have passed away some time over the past couple of months. A gardener was working on one of the flowerbeds in the garden, and the two exchanged nods as they noticed each other.

"Such a shame, about Joe," she said, indicating the sign.

The man frowned, "Er...yes," he said slowly, "Not that I knew him, of course."

"Didn't' you? Well, he certainly left an amazing legacy in this park."

"That he did," said the gardener, and resumed his task.

Katie carried on walking round, and at bench three, looked once more for the inscription.

'For Betsy and Fred Butterworth, who loved the view from this bench. Gone but not forgotten' it said. She wondered what was going on. Where were her benches? She quickened her step to bench four. 'In memory of Robert Dodd, January 1945 – August 1999. RIP' said the inscription. Katie's mind started to race. She hurried on past benches five, six and seven, which all had dedications to people who had passed away. Realisation was beginning to dawn, as she broke into a run past the remaining benches, which all had dedications she had never seen before. As the last bench came into view she slowed down, and a huge wave of relief swept over her as she saw a lone figure sitting there. She rushed towards him.

"Mr Smith!" she cried in delight, "Oh, sorry...my mistake," she added as the stranger turned round.

"That's all right my dear," said the elderly man cheerfully, "You look like you've been running! I'm just going now so you can sit here and catch your breath until your Mr Smith arrives."

"Thank you," said Katie, and as the man stood up, the inscription on the bench came into full view.

> 'In memory of Mr John Smith, 1905 – 1978
> Entrepreneur & philanthropist whose vision
> and generosity created this park
> "I gave you wings, but you must fly by yourself"'

Katie slumped on to the park bench and ran her fingers along the carved wooden letters. 'I gave you wings, but you must fly by yourself'. Softly, tears began to fall as the words sank in. But how would she manage without Mr Smith? She didn't know how long she had been sitting there until at last, she wiped away her tears, and looked up at the clear blue sky.

"Thank you for my wings, Mr Smith," she said silently, "I am flying."

Suddenly she became aware of the rustling of paper nearby. A woman had sat down at the other end of the bench and was opening a sandwich. Katie laughed inwardly when she saw it was from the deli on the high street.

The woman glanced at her, and Katie tilted her head in greeting, before saying, "Beautiful day, isn't it?"

The woman looked about her as if it was the first time she had noticed the weather.

Katie went on, "A perfect day for sitting on a park bench."

"Is it?" replied the woman.

"Better than you might imagine," said Katie, breaking into a smile. "Let me introduce myself. I'm Katie..."

The End

For more information and resources:
www.beyondtheparkgates.com
www.pen-life.co.uk
Pen-Life Chartered Financial Planners
Tudor Court, Opus Avenue, York, YO26 6RS
Tel: 0800 1072178
Email: helen@pen-life.co.uk